READ WELL®
FLUENCY FOUNDATIONS

My Activity Book
Units A–E

Decoding Practice
Comprehension and Skill Work

Cambium
LEARNING®

BOSTON, MA | LONGMONT, CO

Read Well is a registered trademark of Sopris West Educational Services.

ISBN-13: 978-1-60218-516-6
ISBN-10: 1-60218-516-1

166764/1-10

Printed in the United States of America

Published and Distributed by

Cambium
LEARNING®
Sopris West®

4093 Specialty Place • Longmont, CO 80504 • 303-651-2829

www.sopriswest.com

ILLUSTRATION CREDITS
Cover   Raccoon illustrated by Clark Tate.

1, 4-8: illustrated by Clark Tate. 3: lion illustrated by Clark Tate. 3: weeds, hats, rats, and deer ©Jupiter Images. 9, 23, 35, 47, 59: illustrated by Eldon Doty. 11, 15, 27, 51: ©Jupiter Images. 13, 17, 20: illustrated by Graham Francious. 25, 28, 29, 32, 33, 36: illustrated by Maurie Manning. 37-45: illustrated by Liz Wolf. 49, 53, 56, 57: illustrated by Kathryn Mitter.

Table of Contents

Name _____

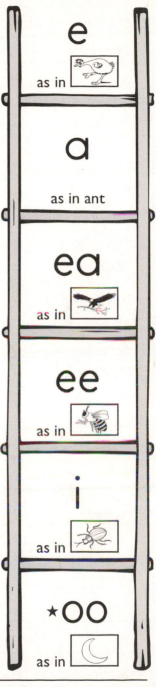

e
as in

a
as in ant

ea
as in

ee
as in

i
as in

★ oo
as in

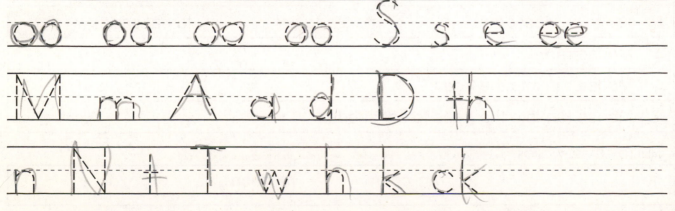

oo oo oo oo S s e ee

M m A a d D th

n N t T w h k ck

Name _____

★ **1. FOCUS/REVIEW SOUNDS** Use the Sound Ladder on page 1 to introduce the focus sound, /oo/ as in moon, and to review sounds.

2. SHIFTY WORD BLENDING For each word, have students say the underlined part, sound out smoothly, then read the word.

w i n	w i n k	w i n d

3. ACCURACY/FLUENCY For each column, have students say any underlined part, then read each word. Next, have students read the whole column.

A1 Focus Sound Practice	B1 Sound Practice	C1 Rhyming Words	D1 Word Endings	E1 Tricky Words
too	sweet	he	weeds	★ do
moon	deer	me	snacks	★ to
soon	teeth	she	hats	★ into
noon			seeds	★ are
	ran	sack	smacks	
hoot	trash	snack	trees	was
shoot	and	smack		said
scoot			**D2** Contractions	
toot	near	eat	it is	could
moose	stream	meat	it's	couldn't
swoosh		treat		
	swish		I am	is
	this		I'm	isn't
	with			

4. TRICKY WORD GRID *(optional)* Have students read the first row for accuracy, then read the entire grid for fluency.

could	his	the	as	are	5
his	could	are	the	as	10
as	his	are	could	the	15
the	are	could	his	as	20

5. PHRASES AND SENTENCES Have students read each row for accuracy, then fluency.

A	Moose ran	into the trees	to eat seeds
B	Moose ran.		
C	Moose ran into the trees.		
D	Moose ran into the trees to eat seeds.		

6. MULTISYLLABIC WORDS Have students loop under and read each word part, then read each whole word.

rac coon   raccoon

Unit A Activity 1
Use after Decoding Practice 1 and Chapter 1

Name _____

★Vocabulary

A lion is a **carnivore**.
Carnivores eat mostly meat.

Read the sentence below. Read the words above the pictures and write the words that best complete the sentence. End the sentence with a period. Circle the correct picture.

could eat __deer__ and __rats__

weeds	hats	rats	deer

★Tricky Words

For each word, read, spell, write, and ✓. Then draw a happy face in the circle.

	Read, Spell, and ✓	Spell, Write, and ✓	Spell, Write, and ✓	Smile!
1	to ☐	to ☑	to ☑	☺
2	do ☑	do ☑	do ☑	☹
3	into ☑	into ☑	into ☑	☺
4	the ☑	the ☑	the ☑	◯
5	could ☑	could ☑	could ☑	◯

← Go back to page 1

Name _____

★ 1. FOCUS/REVIEW SOUNDS Use the Sound Cards to introduce the focus sound, /ar/ as in shark, and to review selected sounds.

2. SHIFTY WORD BLENDING For each word, have students say the underlined part, sound out smoothly, then read the word.

w i n	t i n	t ee n	t ee th

3. ACCURACY/FLUENCY For each column, have students say any underlined part, then read each word. Next, have students read the whole column.

A1 Focus Sound Practice	B1 Buildups	C1 Rhyming Words	D1 Shifty Words	E1 Tricky Words
art	moo	and	soon	are
dart	moon	sand	seen	is
smart	moons	stand	seem	his
start			see	has
	too	ear		
dark	tooth	hear	with	do
Mark		near	wish	to
shark	did			into
sharks	didn't	**C2** Mixed Practice	swish	
	B2 Word Endings	neat	swoosh	could
	hoots	room		would
	weeds	deer		should
	seeds	this		
	snacks	need		said
	eats	swam		

4. PHRASES AND SENTENCES Have students read each row for accuracy, then fluency.

A	the trash can	has a sweet stink	said Raccoon

B The trash can . . .

C The trash can has a sweet stink.

D "The trash can has a sweet stink," said Raccoon.

5. MULTISYLLABIC WORDS Have students loop under and read each word part, then read each whole word.

in deed	indeed
rac coon	raccoon

Unit A Activity 2
Use after Decoding Practice 2 and Chapter 2

Name _____

I listened to my partner read today's chapter.   Signed _____

★Rhyming Patterns

For each box, read the rhyming pattern at the top. Trace the beginning sounds and write the patterns to make words. Read the words to yourself.

at	oot	ark
c at	sh oot	d ark
s at	h oot	m ack
r at	t oo t	sh ack

★Sentence Jumble

Use the words in each box to make a sentence. Start each sentence with a capital letter. End each sentence with a period.

Moose weeds eats	Moose eats weeds.
seeds eats he	He eat eeds

Read the sentences. Draw a happy face if they make sense. ◯

Unit A Activity 3
Use after Decoding Practice 2 and Chapter 2

Name _____

★ Building Fluency

Sentence Reading: Read each sentence 3 times and cross out a deer each time you read the sentence.

Moose eats weeds.

Moose eats weeds and seeds.

Meat is a treat.

Meat is a treat, a sweet, sweet treat.

Deer snacks and smacks.

Deer snacks and smacks and eats.

Deer snacks and smacks and eats with his teeth.

"I seek seeds."

"I seek seeds and weeds too."

"I seek seeds and weeds too," said Moose.

Handwriting: For each letter or letter pattern, trace and then copy in the blank space. At the end of each row, draw a happy face to show that you did your best work.

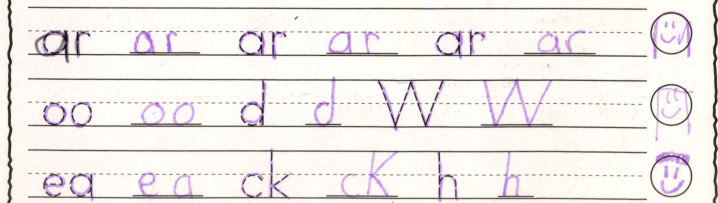

Name _____

★ 1. FOCUS SOUND Use the Sound Card to introduce the focus sound, /wh/ as in whale.

2. SOUND REVIEW Have students review the sounds for accuracy. **Cross Out Game:** Have students say and cross out each /wh/. Repeat for /ar/ and /o͞o/.

ar	i	o͞o	wh	a	ar	i	7
o͞o	wh	a	ar	i	o͞o	wh	14

3. SHIFTY WORD BLENDING For each word, have students say the underlined part, sound out smoothly, then read the word.

h a <u>m</u>	h a <u>t</u>	h a <u>ck</u>	<u>wh</u> a ck

4. ACCURACY/FLUENCY For each column, have students say any underlined part, then read each word. Next, have students read the whole column.

A1 Focus Sound Practice	**B1** Rhyming Words	**C1** Mixed Practice	**D1** Shifty Words	**E1** Tricky Words
<u>wh</u>am	ick	dream	wi<u>n</u>	★ what
<u>wh</u>oosh	sick	sweet	wi<u>nk</u>	want
<u>wh</u>ack	Rick	deer	<u>s</u>ink	are
A2 Sound Practice	am	steam	<u>st</u>ink	do
Moose	ham	smart		to
too	wham	sea	t<u>oo</u>th	said
		Mark	t<u>ee</u>th	is
star	neat	**C2** Contractions	**D2** Word Endings	was
hard	treat	can	<u>swims</u>	wasn't
car		can't	<u>stinks</u>	would
dark	crash		<u>mints</u>	wouldn't
	trash	that	<u>smacks</u>	should
	dash	that's	<u>needs</u>	shouldn't
			<u>drinks</u>	

5. PHRASES AND SENTENCES Have students read each row for accuracy, then fluency.

Ⓐ	Raccoon and Moose	want weeds	to eat
Ⓑ	Raccoon and Moose . . .		
Ⓒ	Raccoon and Moose want weeds.		
Ⓓ	Raccoon and Moose want weeds to eat.		

6. MULTISYLLABIC WORDS Have students loop under and read each word part, then read each whole word.

car toon	cartoon	rac coon	raccoon

Unit A Activity 4
Use after Decoding Practice 3 and Chapter 3

Name _____

I listened to my partner read today's chapter.   Signed _____

★Story Comprehension
Song and Dance Routine

Read each sentence. Fill in the bubble for the answer. Then write it in the blank.

1 Moose, [lion], and ___Raccoon___ want to win.
  ○ Deer   ○ Trees   ◉ Raccoon

2 Deer said, "This is ___hard___."
  ○ smack   ◉ hard   ○ mean

3 "We need to ___see___," said [owl].
  ○ start   ○ dream   ◉ see

4 Raccoon said, "What a ___treat___!"
  ○ indeed   ○ neat   ○ treat

★Handwriting Fluency

Copy the sentence. Then illustrate it.

Raccoon eats weeds and ham.

Raccoon eats
weeds and ham.

Unit A Activity 5
Use after Decoding Practice 3 and Chapter 3

Name _____

Building Fluency

★**Passage Reading:**

1. Read the story 2 times. Cross out a shark each time you read the story.

Mack the Shark

Mack the mean shark swims in the sea.   8
Mack needs to eat.   12
It is too dark to see.   18

Mack the mean shark sees a sea treat.   26
Is it meat?   29
It is too dark to see.   35

Mack the mean shark has teeth, teeth, teeth.   43
Whoosh! Whack! Wham!   46
It is too dark to see.   52

Mack the mean shark whacks the sea treat.   60
Oo! It wasn't meat.   64
It is too dark to see.   70

Mack the mean shark swims in the sea.   78
His tooth is in the sand.   84
It was too dark to see.   90

2. Set a timer and read as far as you can in one minute.
   Cross out the timer.

Handwriting: Trace and then copy the sentence. At the end of each row, draw a happy face to show that you did your best work.

Sharks swim in the sea.

Name _____

1. SOUND REVIEW Have students review sounds for accuracy, then for fluency.

ar	oo	i	a	wh	ar	oo	7
a	i	wh	ar	oo	i	a	14

2. SHIFTY WORD BLENDING For each word, have students say the underlined part, sound out smoothly, then read the word.

s <u>a</u> t   s <u>i</u> t   s <u>ea</u> t

3. ACCURACY/FLUENCY For each column, have students say any underlined part, then read each word. Next, have students read the whole column.

A1 Mixed Practice	B1 Mixed Practice	C1 Shifty Words	D1 Word Endings	E1 Tricky Words
whoosh	near	<u>sn</u>ack	<u>trees</u>	is
shark	creek	<u>sm</u>ack	<u>scats</u>	isn't
hard	three	<u>sm</u>ack<u>s</u>	<u>wants</u>	
treat	this		<u>stars</u>	what
seek	add	<u>h</u>oo<u>t</u>	<u>swims</u>	are
ant	stinks	<u>sh</u>oot		was
whack	wink	<u>sc</u>oot		want

4. PHRASES AND SENTENCES Have students read each row for accuracy, then fluency.

A	said the man	at noon	want to eat	can eat a snack
B	the ant and shark		can eat a treat	near the stream

C The ant and shark . . .

D The ant and shark can eat a treat.

E The ant and shark can eat a treat near the stream.

5. MULTISYLLABIC WORDS Have students loop under and read each word part, then read each whole word.

rac coon   raccoon   car toon   cartoon   in deed   indeed

6. SOUND DICTATION Have students say and write each sound.

a. _oo_   b. _ar_   c. _wh_   d. _e_   e. _a_

7. TRICKY WORD DICTATION Have students say and spell each word, then say, spell, and write it.

a. _to_   b. _do_   c. _into_   d. _could_

Unit A Activity 6
Use after Decoding Practice 4 and Chapter 4

Name _____

I listened to my partner read today's chapter.   Signed _____

★Phrases I Can Read

Fill in the bubble for the words that tell about each picture.

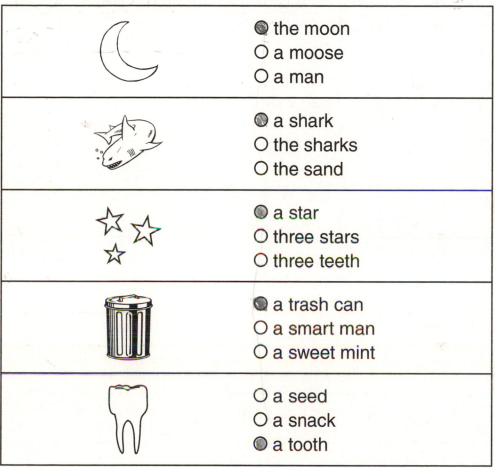

● the moon	
○ a moose	
○ a man	
● a shark	
○ the sharks	
○ the sand	
● a star	
○ three stars	
○ three teeth	
● a trash can	
○ a smart man	
○ a sweet mint	
○ a seed	
○ a snack	
● a tooth	

★Tricky Words in Sentences

Read each sentence. Fill in the bubble for the correct answer and write the word in the blank.

1   "What ____should____ we eat?" said Moose.
    ● should   ○ was   ○ to

2   It was dark. The mean shark ____couldn't____ see.
    ○ said   ● couldn't   ○ wasn't

3   Deer said, "Raccoon ____was____ a hoot."
    ● was   ○ should   ○ said

Unit A Activity 7
Use after Decoding Practice 4 and Chapter 4

Name _____

★ Story Retell

Fill in the bubble for the sentence or word that best retells the beginning, middle, and end of the story. Then read and illustrate each part of the story.

BEGINNING ●	◉ Moose said, "Weeds, weeds, weeds, snacks to eat." ○ [owl] said, "I can swim."	
MIDDLE ■	○ [lion] said, "I need meat, meat, meat!" ○ Raccoon said, "We need to swim."	
END ▲	Raccoon said, "Weeds and ham are sweet." Deer said, "Raccoon wins. He is the ___star___." ◉ star ○ trash	

Handwriting Fluency

Trace the sentence.

That trash can stinks.

Name _____

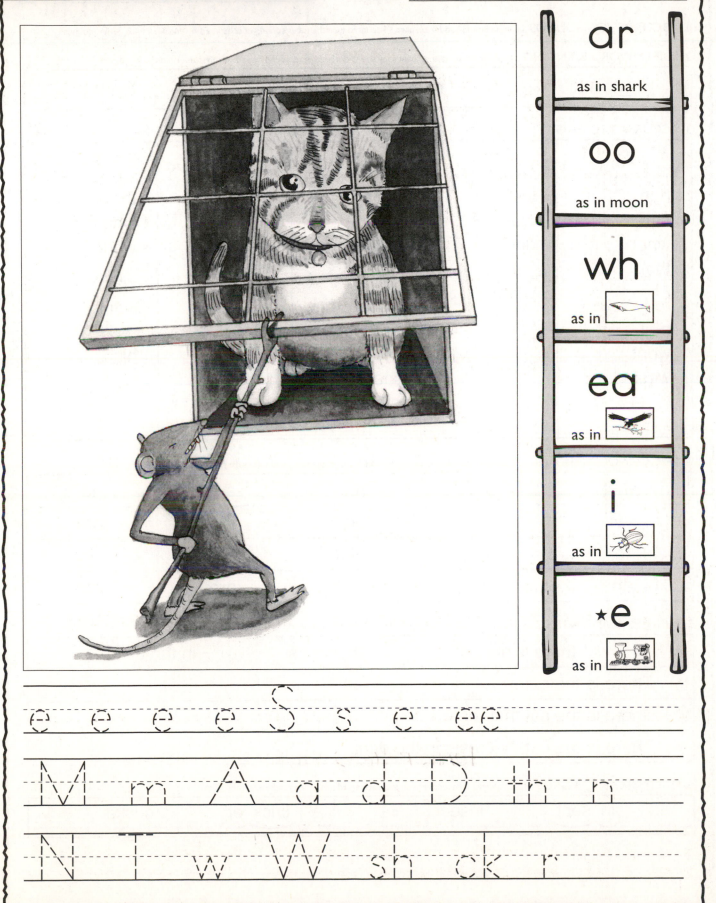

ar
as in shark

oo
as in moon

wh
as in

ea
as in

i
as in

★e
as in

Name _____

★1. FOCUS/REVIEW SOUNDS Use the Sound Ladder on page 13 to introduce the focus sound, /ĕĕĕ/ as in Ed or engine, and to review sounds.

2. SHIFTY WORD BLENDING For each word, have students say the underlined part, sound out smoothly, then read the word.

w̲ink	r̲ink	d̲rink	th̲ink

3. ACCURACY/FLUENCY For each column, have students say any underlined part, then read each word. Next, have students read the whole column.

A1 Focus Sound Practice	B1 Mixed Practice	C1 Shifty Words	D1 Word Endings	E1 Tricky Words
h̲en	w̲ith	s̲oon	ant̲s	★ there
d̲en	hi̲ss	m̲oon	seed̲s	★ where
wh̲en	da̲rk	m̲ean	star̲s	★ work
th̲en	thi̲s		treat̲s	
	wh̲am	e̲at	need̲s	was
red	ca̲n't	wh̲eat	sweet̲s	want
met	th̲at	n̲eat	asked̲	is
went	re̲ad	near		his
west		sh̲ear		
				should
				could

4. TRICKY WORD GRID (optional) Have students read the first row for accuracy, then read the entire grid for fluency.

what	do	into	are	to	5
into	what	do	to	are	10
to	are	into	what	do	15
do	to	what	are	into	20

5. PHRASES AND SENTENCES Have students read each row for accuracy, then fluency.

A	there is the cat that rests in the den
B	There is the cat.
C	There is the cat that rests.
D	There is the cat that rests in the den.

6. MULTISYLLABIC WORDS Have students loop under and read each word part, then read each whole word.

in sect	insect	crick et	cricket

Name _____

Vocabulary

Main characters are who the story is about.

Read the sentence below. Read the words above the pictures and write the words that best complete the sentence. End the sentence with a period. Circle the correct picture.

The main characters in our story are a _____ and an _____

teeth	cricket	ham	ant

Tricky Words

For each word, read, spell, write, and ✓. Then draw a happy face in the circle.

	Read, Spell, and ✓	Spell, Write, and ✓	Spell, Write, and ✓	Smile!
1	there ☐	__ __ __ __ __ ☐	_____ ☐	◯
2	are ☐	__ __ __ ☐	_____ ☐	◯
3	where ☐	__ __ __ __ __ ☐	_____ ☐	◯
4	would ☐	__ __ __ __ __ ☐	_____ ☐	◯
5	what ☐	__ __ __ __ ☐	_____ ☐	◯

⬅ Go back to page 13

★ 1. FOCUS/REVIEW SOUNDS Use the Sound Cards to introduce the focus sound, /ī/ as in fly, and to review selected sounds.

2. SHIFTY WORD BLENDING For each word, have students say the underlined part, sound out smoothly, then read the word.

n e s<u>t</u>	<u>w</u>e s t	w e <u>n</u> t	<u>d</u> e n t

3. ACCURACY/FLUENCY For each column, have students say any underlined part, then read each word. Next, have students read the whole column.

A1 Focus Sound Practice	**B1** Sound Practice	**C1** Word Endings	**D1** Shifty Words	**E1** Tricky Words
m<u>y</u>	nest	<u>scoot</u>ed	r<u>i</u>nk	★ <u>aren't</u>
cr<u>y</u>	west	<u>need</u>ed	s<u>i</u>nk	★ <u>what</u>'s
dr<u>y</u>	test	<u>rest</u>ed	th<u>i</u>nk	★ who
tr<u>y</u>		<u>seat</u>ed	th<u>a</u>nk	
	went	<u>ask</u>ed	thank<u>s</u>	there
sh<u>y</u>	sent	<u>treat</u>ed		where
wh<u>y</u>			<u>a</u>m	
sk<u>y</u>	ten	**C2** Mixed Practice	h<u>a</u>m	want
	when	r<u>oo</u>m	h<u>i</u>m	wants
	then	tr<u>ea</u>ts	<u>K</u>im	
		sw<u>ee</u>t		wasn't
		<u>S</u>eth		hasn't
		sna<u>ck</u>		
		h<u>ar</u>d		

4. PHRASES AND SENTENCES Have students read each row for accuracy, then fluency.

A	where is	the shy cat	with the sweet treat
B	Where is . . .		
C	Where is the shy cat?		
D	Where is the shy cat with the sweet treat?		

5. RHYMING WORDS Have students read each word set for accuracy, then fluency. Ask how the words are the same.

art	tart	start	cart	at	cat	sat	scat
ash	cash	crash	trash	me	he		tee hee

6. MULTISYLLABIC WORDS Have students loop under and read each word part, then read each whole word.

kit ten	kitten	rac coon	raccoon

Unit B Activity 2
Use after Decoding Practice 2 and Chapter 2

Name _____

I listened to my partner read today's chapter.   Signed _____

Rhyming Patterns

For each box, read the rhyming pattern at the top. Trace the beginning sounds and write the patterns to make words. Read the words to yourself.

art	ank	ish
st_____	t_____	d_____
d_____	th_____	sw_____
sm_____	dr_____	w_____

Sentence Jumble

Use the words in each box to make a sentence. Start each sentence with a capital letter. End each sentence with a period.

sad was Cricket	_____ _____
Cricket cry Ant could hear	_____ _____

Read the sentences. Draw a happy face if they make sense.

Unit B Activity 3
Use after Decoding Practice 2 and Chapter 2

Name _____

Building Fluency

★**Word Reading:** Read the words down each column and ✓ the box. Read the words across each row and ✓ the box. Then set a timer for one minute. See if you can beat the timer reading all the words in one minute. Draw a happy face when you beat the timer.

hen	my	dark	tank	meat	☐
ten	cry	Mark	drank	neat	☐
when	try	shark	sank	seat	☐
den	sky	card	rank	heat	☐
then	shy	hard	Hank	treat	☐
☐	☐	☐	☐	☐	◯

Sentence Reading: Read each sentence 3 times and cross out a cricket each time you read the sentence.

Cricket sat.

Cricket sat near Ant's nest.

Cricket sat near Ant's nest and shed a tear.

Ant went.

Ant went to Cricket.

Ant went to Cricket with ten seeds.

Handwriting: For each letter, letter pattern, or word, trace and then copy in the blank space. At the end of each row, draw a happy face to show that you did your best work.

my _____ cry _____ shy _____ ◯

cry _____ e _____ oo _____ ◯

Unit B Decoding Practice 3
Use with The Hen and the Bucket

Name _____

1. SOUND REVIEW Have students review the sounds for accuracy. **Cross Out Game:** Have students say and cross out each /lll/. Repeat for /ĭĭĭ/ and /ĕĕĕ/.

| e | wh | l | -y | ar | wh | e | 7 |
| l | -y | ar | e | wh | l | -y | 14 |

2. SHIFTY WORD BLENDING For each word, have students say the underlined part, sound out smoothly, then read the word.

<u>h</u>ill   <u>w</u>ill   w<u>e</u>ll   <u>s</u>well

3. ACCURACY/FLUENCY For each column, have students say any underlined part, then read each word. Next, have students read the whole column.

A1 Focus Sound Practice	B1 Sound Practice	C1 Rhyming Words	D1 Shifty Words	E1 Tricky Words
<u>l</u>et	my	sell	<u>r</u>ear	★ little
<u>l</u>et's	try	well	<u>d</u>ear	★ look
<u>l</u>and	cry	swell	<u>cl</u>ear	★ one
<u>l</u>ast	why	smell	<u>cl</u>ea<u>n</u>	★ two
<u>l</u>ick		spell		who
<u>l</u>end	hen		**D2** Rhyming Words	
	when	old	tank	aren't
will		told	thank	what's
hill	**B2** Mixed Practice	hold	drank	wasn't
still	stinks			
milk	drink		he	
silk	can't		she	
	Kim		we	
	shed		me	
	last			

4. PHRASES AND SENTENCES Have students read each row for accuracy, then fluency.

| A | the little old kitten | will try | to clean the shed |

B The little old kitten . . .

C The little old kitten will try.

D The little old kitten will try to clean the shed.

5. MULTISYLLABIC WORDS Have students loop under and read each word part, then read each whole word.

crick et   cricket   mit ten   mitten

Unit B Activity 4
Use after Decoding Practice 3 and The Hen and the Bucket

Name _____

I listened to my partner read today's chapter. Signed _____

Story Comprehension
The Hen and the Bucket

Read each sentence. Fill in the bubble for the answer. Then write it in the blank. End each sentence with a period.

1 The little old hen needed a cool _____
   ○ star   ○ hat   ○ drink

2 The little old hen needed to _____
   ○ think   ○ snack   ○ swim

3 The little old hen started to _____
   ○ eat meat   ○ work hard   ○ cry and cry

4 At last the little old hen had a _____
   ○ neat snack   ○ red hat   ○ cool drink

Handwriting Fluency

Copy the sentence. Then illustrate it.

The little rat had a red hat.

_____

- - - - - - - - - - - - - - - - - -

_____

- - - - - - - - - - - - - - - - - -

_____

_____

Unit B Activity 5
Use after Decoding Practice 3 and The Hen and the Bucket

Name _____

Building Fluency

Passage Reading:

1. Read the story 2 times. Cross out a hat each time you read the story.

Hen Needs a Nest

    Hen needed a nest. She went to work in the shed.   11
Hen worked hard. She needed a nest to rest.   20

    Cricket scooted into the shed. "Hen," he said, "why   29
work hard? Rest, Hen, rest."   34

    Hen said, "I could rest. I need a cool drink." Then Hen   46
and Cricket went to the creek. Hen and Cricket had a cool drink.   59
Then Hen said, "I had a cool drink. I need a sweet treat."   72

    "Seeds are sweet," said Cricket. Hen and Cricket had a   82
snack.   83

    Soon the sky was dark. Hen still needed a rest. She   94
started to work. She worked in the dark. Soon she would rest in   107
the nest.   109

---

2. Set a timer and read as far as you can in one minute.
   Cross out the timer.

Handwriting: Trace and then copy the sentence. At the end of each row, draw a happy face to show that you did your best work.

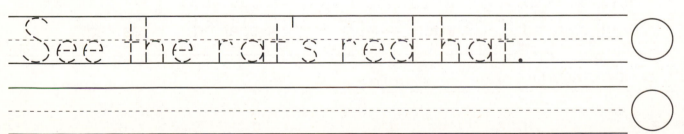

1. SOUND REVIEW Have students review sounds for accuracy, then for fluency.

-y	wh	ar	e	l	-y	6
ar	ar	e	wh	l	-y	12

2. SHIFTY WORD BLENDING For each word, have students say the underlined part, sound out smoothly, then read the word.

r<u>i</u>nk   <u>dr</u>ink   dr<u>a</u>nk

3. ACCURACY/FLUENCY For each column, have students say any underlined part, then read each word. Next, have students read the whole column.

A1 Mixed Practice	B1 Mixed Practice	C1 Rhyming Words	D1 Shifty Words	E1 Tricky Words
snack	Mark	end	th<u>ank</u>	look
noon	than	lend	th<u>i</u>nk	one
swell	trash	send	<u>dr</u>ink	two
shy	three	**C2** Mixed Practice	dr<u>a</u>nk	**E2** Contractions
started	hand	smack	<u>s</u>ank	<u>what</u>'s
let's	shack	smart		<u>didn</u>'t
scoot	near	smell		<u>it</u>'s
end	test			

4. PHRASES AND SENTENCES Have students read each row for accuracy, then fluency.

A	a little old man	went to see	look at me	let him eat
B	the hen wants to eat	a little snack	in the room	
C	The hen wants to eat.			
D	The hen wants to eat a little snack.			
E	The hen wants to eat a little snack in the room.			

5. MULTISYLLABIC WORDS Have students loop under and read each word part, then read each whole word.

start ed   started   seat ed   seated

6. SOUND DICTATION Have students say and write each sound.

a. _____   b. _____   c. _____   d. _____   e. _____

7. TRICKY WORD DICTATION Have students say and spell each word, then say, spell, and write it.

a. _____   b. _____   c. _____   d. _____

Unit B Activity 6
Use after Decoding Practice 4 and The Cat and the Rat

Name _____

I listened to my partner read today's chapter.   Signed _____

★Sentences I Can Read

Fill in the bubble for the sentence that best tells about each picture.

○ The little rat is cool in his red hat.
○ The little rat hits the cat.

○ Mack the shark eats meat.
○ Mack the shark eats little trees.

○ The little rat eats meat and weeds.
○ The little rat drinks milk and eats seeds.

Tricky Words in Sentences

Read each sentence. Fill in the bubble for the correct answer and write the word in the blank.

1 The rat and the cat _____ in the shed.
   ○ said   ○ aren't   ○ could

2 _____ the little sweet treat?
   ○ As   ○ Into   ○ What's

3 Raccoon and Moose _____ to eat a snack.
   ○ there   ○ where   ○ want

Unit B Activity 7
Use after Decoding Practice 4 and The Cat and the Rat

Name _____

Story Retell
The Cat and the Rat

Fill in the bubble for the sentence that best retells the beginning, middle, and end of the story. Then read and illustrate each part of the story.

BEGINNING ●	○ The cat didn't eat the shark. ○ The cat didn't eat the little rat.	
MIDDLE ■	○ The sad cat started to cry. ○ The sad cat ran into the trees.	
END ▲	○ The rat said, "I will work hard." And he did. ○ The rat said, "I will not work." And he went to rest.	

Handwriting Fluency

Trace the sentence.

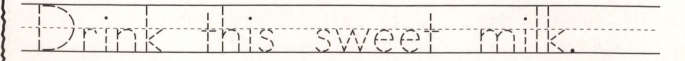

Drink this sweet milk.

Name _____

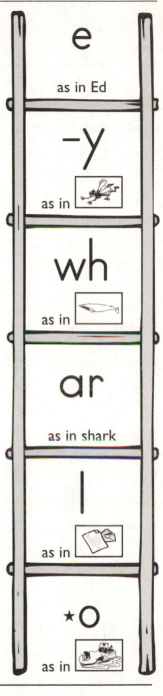

e
as in Ed

-y
as in

wh
as in

ar
as in shark

l
as in

★o
as in

o o o o

ar ck a oo e fi sh ck

why

Name _____

★1. FOCUS/REVIEW SOUNDS Use the Sound Ladder on page 25 to introduce the focus sound, /ŏŏŏ/ as in otter, and to review sounds.

2. SHIFTY WORD BLENDING For each word, have students say the underlined part, sound out smoothly, then read the word.

m <u>ee</u> t	m <u>ea</u> t	<u>s</u> ea t	s ea <u>m</u>

3. ACCURACY/FLUENCY For each column, have students say any underlined part, then read each word. Next, have students read the whole column.

A1 Focus Sound Practice	B1 Sound Practice	C1 Rhyming Words	D1 Shifty Words	E1 Tricky Words
l<u>o</u>t	them	sand	Ki<u>t</u>	★ looks
m<u>o</u>m	met	land	ki<u>d</u>	★ they
l<u>o</u>st			ki<u>ck</u>	★ no
R<u>o</u>d	my	wish	**D2** Mixed Practice	
	shy	dish		where
on	cry	**C2** Word Endings	<u>th</u>em	are
lot			wi<u>th</u>	two
moth	cool	<u>tell</u>s	s<u>ee</u>s	one
shot	room	<u>think</u>s		
not	mood	<u>added</u>		what
		<u>nod</u>s		what's

4. TRICKY WORD GRID (optional) Have students read the first row for accuracy, then read the entire grid for fluency.

who	little	there	they	where	5
they	there	where	little	who	10
little	there	they	who	where	15
there	where	little	they	who	20

5. PHRASES AND SENTENCES Have students read each row for accuracy, then fluency.

A	Rod went near the cat the shy cat ran to the sandlot
B	Rod went near the cat.
C	The shy cat ran to the sandlot.
D	Rod went near the cat, and the shy cat ran to the sandlot.

6. MULTISYLLABIC WORDS Have students loop under and read each word part, then read each whole word.

<u>sand lot</u>	sandlot	<u>scoot ted</u>	scooted

Unit C Activity 1
Use after Decoding Practice 1 and Chapter 1

Name _____

Vocabulary

A **mood** is the way you feel.
You can be in a good mood or a bad mood.

★Read each sentence and circle the happy face for a good mood or the sad face for a bad mood. Cross out the wrong answer.

		good mood	bad mood
1	I want a cat. Mom said, "No cats!"	😃	😠
2	I did well on a test.	😃	😠
3	My team wins!	😃	😠
4	I am sick.	😃	😠

Tricky Words

For each word, read, spell, write, and ✓. Then draw a happy face in the circle.

	Read, Spell, and ✓	Spell, Write, and ✓	Spell, Write, and ✓	Smile!
1	look ☐	__ __ __ __ ☐	_____ ☐	◯
2	one ☐	__ __ __ ☐	_____ ☐	◯
3	who ☐	__ __ __ ☐	_____ ☐	◯
4	little ☐	__ __ __ __ __ __ ☐	_____ ☐	◯
5	two ☐	__ __ __ ☐	_____ ☐	◯

◁ Go back to page 25

Name _____

★ 1. FOCUS/REVIEW SOUNDS Use the Sound Cards to introduce the focus sound, /all/ as in ball, and to review selected sounds.

2. SHIFTY WORD BLENDING For each word, have students say the underlined part, sound out smoothly, then read the word.

c a <u>n</u>	c a <u>t</u>	<u>m</u> a t	M a <u>tt</u>

3. ACCURACY/FLUENCY For each column, have students say any underlined part, then read each word. Next, have students read the whole column.

A1 Focus Sound Practice	**B1** Sound Practice	**C1** Rhyming Words	**D1** Shifty Words	**E1** Tricky Words
<u>b</u>ack	Mom	card	b<u>e</u>t	★ because
<u>b</u>lack	not	hard	b<u>i</u>t	★ there's
<u>B</u>eth	Rod's		<u>hi</u>t	what's
<u>b</u>last		my		
<u>b</u>est	Tenth	shy	**D2** Mixed Practice	**E2** Contractions
<u>b</u>e	let		St<u>ree</u>t	is not
	Let's	Bill	t<u>ea</u>m	isn't
<u>all</u>		will	s<u>o</u>b	
m<u>all</u>	**B2** Word Endings		r<u>i</u>b	was not
b<u>all</u>	think<u>s</u>	old	<u>B</u>ob	wasn't
c<u>all</u>	need<u>s</u>	cold	cr<u>a</u>b	
	hear<u>s</u>	bold	<u>A</u>nn	has not
	meet<u>s</u>		w<u>e</u>nt	hasn't
	want<u>s</u>	me	<u>th</u>is	
		be		

4. PHRASES AND SENTENCES Have students read each row for accuracy, then fluency.

A	Beth and Rod	will meet	to hit balls
B	Beth and Rod . . .		
C	Beth and Rod will meet.		
D	Beth and Rod will meet to hit balls.		

5. MULTISYLLABIC WORDS Have students loop under and read each word part, then read each whole word.

bob cats   bobcats   Bobcats
neat ness   neatness

Unit C Activity 2
Use after Decoding Practice 2 and Chapter 2

Name _____

I listened to my partner read today's chapter. Signed _____

Rhyming Patterns

For each box, read the rhyming pattern at the top. Trace the beginning sounds and write the pattern to make words. Read the words to yourself.

eat	ill	-y
m_____	B_____	m_____
s_____	w_____	sh_____
tr_____	st_____	cr_____

Sentence Jumble

Use the words in each box to make a sentence. Start each sentence with a capital letter. End each sentence with a period.

the Bobcats a team are	_____ _____
can hit Rod and Beth the ball	_____ _____ _____

Read the sentences. Draw a happy face if they make sense. ◯

Unit C Activity 3
Use after Decoding Practice 2 and Chapter 2

Name _____

Building Fluency

Sentence Reading: Read each sentence 3 times and cross out a baseball each time you read the sentence.

Whack! Rod hit the ball.

Whack! Rod hit the ball into the trees.

Can Matt whack the ball?

Can Matt whack the ball into the trees?

Let's meet at the sandlot.

Let's meet at the sandlot to hit balls.

Let's meet at the sandlot to hit balls with the team.

Rod will meet his team.

Rod will meet his team at the sandlot.

Rod will meet his team at the sandlot and hit balls.

Handwriting: For each letter, letter pattern, or word, trace and then copy in the blank space. At the end of each row, draw a happy face to show that you did your best work.

all _____ all _____ b _____ b _____ ◯

sly _____ o _____ e _____ l _____ ◯

oo _____ Th _____ N _____ ◯

Name _____

1. SOUND REVIEW Have students review the sounds for accuracy. **Cross Out Game:** Have students say and cross out each /g/. Repeat for /b/, /ŏŏŏ/, /fff/.

l	b	o	g	l	f	o	7
g	l	f	b	f	o	g	14

2. SHIFTY WORD BLENDING For each word, have students say the underlined part, sound out smoothly, then read the word.

m y	<u>sh</u> y	<u>wh</u> y

3. ACCURACY/FLUENCY For each column, have students say any underlined part, then read each word. Next, have students read the whole column.

A1 **Focus Sound Practice**	B1 **Mixed Practice**	C1 **Rhyming Words**	D1 **Shifty Words**	E1 **Tricky Words**
<u>g</u>et	blast	whack	<u>s</u>it	★ good
<u>g</u>lad	loss	shack	<u>h</u>it	work
<u>g</u>rins	ball			★ worked
be<u>g</u>	wind	team	mi<u>tt</u>	want
	dash	ream	<u>M</u>a<u>tt</u>	★ wanted
stron<u>g</u>		cream		
swin<u>g</u>	**B2** **Word Endings**	scream	**D2** **Mixed Practice**	no
	<u>tr</u>ees		shot	★ so
<u>fl</u>y	<u>nod</u>ded		cool	★ go
<u>f</u>ast	<u>Bobc</u>ats		best	
<u>f</u>ar			hard	because
le<u>ft</u>			told	want
				where

4. PHRASES AND SENTENCES Have students read each row for accuracy, then fluency.

A	the tall lad	hit the ball	it went	into the trees
B	The tall lad hit the ball.			
C	It went into the trees.			
D	The tall lad hit the ball, and it went into the trees.			

5. MULTISYLLABIC WORDS Have students loop under and read each word part, then read each whole word.

soft ball	softball	grand dad	granddad
fan tas tic	fantastic	be gan	began

Unit C Activity 4
Use after Decoding Practice 3 and Chapter 3

Name _____

I listened to my partner read today's chapter.   Signed _____

Story Comprehension
Bobcat Rod

Read each sentence. Fill in the bubble for the answer. Then write it in the blank. End each sentence with a period, as needed.

1 Rod said to Mom, "The team _____."
   ○ can swim   ○ will eat   ○ is cool

2 Rod was fast and ran _____
   ○ to see the hen   ○ with the team   ○ near the farm

3 Mom told Rod to get his _____
   ○ bat and mitt   ○ treat   ○ kitten

4 Rod hit the ball _____
   ○ into the trick   ○ into the ham   ○ into the trees

5 "Rod is a Bobcat," said _____
   ○ the sweet treat   ○ the cat   ○ Beth

6 What was Rod's mood at the end?

   Rod was in a _____ mood.
      ○ good
      ○ sad
      ○ bad

Read and check your work. Then draw a happy face in the circle.   ○

Unit C Activity 5
Use after Decoding Practice 3 and Chapter 3

Name _____

Building Fluency

Passage Reading:
1. Read the story 2 times. Cross out a baseball each time you read the story.

The Tenth Street Bobcats

Rod, Beth, Ann, and Matt are Tenth Street   8
Bobcats. The Bobcats are a team. The Bobcats   16
try hard and work hard. The Bobcats can blast the 26
ball into the trees.   30

Beth and Matt sing a team song: 37

    We are the Tenth Street Bobcats.   43
    We try, try, try.   47
    See the ball fly, fly, fly!   53

    We are the Tenth Street Bobcats.   59
    We try, try, try.   63
    The team can hit. My, my, my!   70

    We are the Tenth Street Bobcats.   76
    We try, try, try.   80
    See the ball fly, fly, fly!   86

2. Set a timer and read as far as you can in one minute. Cross out the timer.

Handwriting: Trace and then copy the sentence. At the end of each row, draw a happy face to show that you did your best work.

See the ball fly. _____ ◯

_____ ◯

Unit C Decoding Practice 4
Use with The New Bobcat, Chapter 4

Name _____

1. SOUND REVIEW Have students review sounds for accuracy, then for fluency.

| f | g | b | o | l | f | g | 7 |
| b | o | l | f | g | b | o | 14 |

2. ACCURACY/FLUENCY For each column, have students say any underlined part, then read each word. Next, have students read the whole column.

A1 Mixed Practice	B1 Mixed Practice	C1 Affix Practice	D1 Rhyming Words	E1 Tricky Words
green	blasted	sett<u>le</u>	dog	go
blast	whack	tatt<u>le</u>	clog	no
star	dashes	gigg<u>le</u>	bog	so
twist	beat	**C2** ★ Compound Words	try	wanted
team	smack	softball	why	work
leads	needed	Bobcats	fly	could
clock	whoosh	granddad		because
swing	strong			

3. PHRASES AND SENTENCES Have students read each row for accuracy, then fluency.

A	needed to go beat the clock hit the ball with his mom
B	three frogs went in the bog to get a meal
C	Three frogs went . . .
D	Three frogs went in the bog.
E	Three frogs went in the bog to get a meal.

4. MULTISYLLABIC WORDS Have students loop under and read each word part, then read each whole word.

hall mark hallmark   be gan began   sea weed seaweed

5. SOUND DICTATION Have students say and write each sound.

a. _____ b. _____ c. _____ d. _____ e. _____

6. TRICKY WORD DICTATION Have students say and spell each word, then say, spell, and write it.

a. _____ b. _____ c. _____ d. _____

34

©2009 Sopris West Educational Services. All Rights Reserved.

Name _____

I listened to my partner read today's chapter.   Signed _____

Sentences I Can Read

Fill in the bubble for the sentence that best tells about each picture.

○ Rod hit the ball into the trees.
○ Rod swam with the frogs.

○ Mom swims in the sea.
○ Mom sees the lost ring in the sand.

○ My granddad and I giggle.
○ My granddad and I feed a dog.

Tricky Words in Sentences

Read each sentence. Fill in the bubble for the correct answer and write the word in the blank.

1 The team _____ bats and balls.
   ○ wanted   ○ because   ○ about

2 Beth cannot eat _____ she is sick.
   ○ there's   ○ isn't   ○ because

3 Rod said, "The Sharks _____ cool."
   ○ wasn't   ○ would   ○ are

Unit C Activity 7
Use after Decoding Practice 4 and Chapter 4

Name _____

Story Retell
The New Bobcat

Fill in the bubble for the sentence that best retells the beginning, middle, and end of the story. Then read each part of the story.

BEGINNING ●	○ Rod missed his team. Rod sat in his room in a sad mood. ○ Rod missed his team. Rod sat in the trees in a sad mood.
MIDDLE ■	○ Rod met the team. ○ Rod met Mom. ○ Rod hit with the team. ○ Rod had treats with the team. ○ Rod could not hit the ball. ○ Beth was mad.
END ▲	○ Whack! Rod hit a grand slam! ○ Beth hit the ball into the trees.

Handwriting Fluency

Trace the sentence.

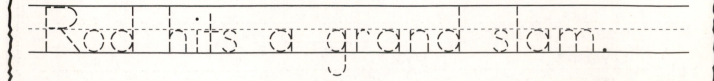

Rod hits a grand slam.

Name _____

f as in frog

g as in

all as in ball

b as in bat

o as in otter

★u as in

u u u u g g g f f f

all ball tall fall hall tall

why

Name _____

★ 1. FOCUS/REVIEW SOUNDS Use the Sound Ladder on page 37 to introduce the focus sound, /ŭŭŭ/ as in umbrella, and to review sounds.

2. SHIFTY WORD BLENDING For each word, have students say the underlined part, sound out smoothly, then read the word.

sang	sing	song	strong

3. ACCURACY/FLUENCY For each column, have students say any underlined part, then read each word. Next, have students read the whole column.

A1 Focus Sound Practice	B1 Mixed Practice	C1 Rhyming Words	D1 Shifty Words	E1 Tricky Words
run	hit	all	not	★ friend
bun	heat	ball	got	★ from
sun	bark	tall	get	★ Harriet
	back		bet	★ of
us	log	sky	best	
dust	little	why		could
must	when		fell	should
cut	hard	sang	feel	
shrug	wind	rang	fee	work
but	rested		free	worked
scrub	men	where's	freed	want
		there's		wanted

4. TRICKY WORD GRID (optional) Have students read the first row for accuracy, then read the entire grid for fluency.

about	because	one	two	go	5
one	go	two	because	about	10
about	one	go	two	because	15
two	one	go	because	about	20

5. PHRASES AND SENTENCES Have students read each row for accuracy, then fluency.

A she worked   in the sun   she cut logs   with the men

B She worked in the sun.

C She cut logs with the men.

D She worked in the sun, and she cut logs with the men.

6. MULTISYLLABIC WORDS Have students loop under and read each word part, then read each whole word.

free dom	freedom	bas ket ball	basketball

Unit D Activity 1
Use after Decoding Practice 1 and Chapter 1

Name _____

Vocabulary

Harriet Tubman was a **slave**.
That means she was owned by someone else.

Read each sentence. Fill in the blank with the word from the bar that best completes each sentence.
End each sentence with a period.

sun	dust	hard	free

1 She had to work _____

2 Harriet had to scrub and _____

3 She cut logs in the _____

4 Harriet said, "I need to be _____."

Tricky Words

For each word, read, spell, write, and ✓. Then draw a happy face in the circle.

	Read, Spell, and ✓	Spell, Write, and ✓	Spell, Write, and ✓	Smile!
1	no ☐	_ _ ☐	___ ☐	◯
2	work ☐	_ _ _ _ ☐	_____ ☐	◯
3	because ☐	_ _ _ _ _ _ _ ☐	_____ ☐	◯
4	so ☐	_ _ ☐	___ ☐	◯
5	about ☐	_ _ _ _ _ ☐	_____ ☐	◯

← Go back to page 37

Name _____

★ 1. FOCUS/REVIEW SOUNDS Use the Sound Cards to introduce the focus sound, /er/ as in sister, and to review selected sounds.

2. SHIFTY WORD BLENDING For each word, have students say the underlined part, sound out smoothly, then read the word.

l e d	l e ss	l a ss	l a s t

3. ACCURACY/FLUENCY For each column, have students say any underlined part, then read each word. Next, have students read the whole column.

A1	B1	C1	D1	E1
Focus Sound Practice	**Sound Practice**	**Rhyming Words**	**Shifty Words**	**Tricky Words**
her	farm	loss	long	★ about
after	star	moss	song	★ story
under	hard	boss	sing	★ for
mister	dark	**C2**	sang	friend
better	**B2**	**Word Endings**	**D2**	★ friends
farther	**Affix Practice**	frees	**Rhyming Words**	work
leader	unless	trees	fun	★ works
darker	unreal	looks	sun	worked
sister	until	looked	run	because
number	**B3**	looking	look	from
	Mixed Practice	asks	took	they
	went	reads	book	who
	bring	fishing		what's
	wish			of
	then			

4. PHRASES AND SENTENCES Have students read each row for accuracy, then fluency.

A	my best friend	wanted to run	in the sand
B	My best friend . . .		
C	My best friend wanted to run.		
D	My best friend wanted to run in the sand.		

5. MULTISYLLABIC WORDS Have students loop under and read each word part, then read each whole word.

Tub man	Tubman
free dom	freedom
to geth er	together

Unit D Activity 2
Use after Decoding Practice 2 and Chapter 2

Name _____

I listened to my partner read today's chapter.   Signed _____

Story Retell
Harriet Tubman Escapes

Fill in the bubble for the phrase or word that best retells the beginning, middle, and end of the story. End each sentence with a period. Then read and illustrate each part of the story.

BEGINNING ● Who?	Tell who the story is about. The story is about _____ _____ ○ Harriet Tubman ○ a man	
MIDDLE ■ Want?	Tell what Harriet wanted. Harriet wanted to _____ ○ see trees ○ be free	
What?	Tell what happened in the story. Harriet ran far to be free. She looked for the star. She looked for the moss. At last, she got to _____ ○ the sea ○ freedom	
END ▲ At the End?	Tell what happened at the end the story. After she was free, Harriet worked hard. She led her friends to _____ ○ freedom ○ the star	

Read and check your work. Then draw a happy face in the circle. ◯

Unit D Activity 3
Use after Decoding Practice 2 and Chapter 2

Name _____

Building Fluency

Word Reading: Read the words down each column and ✓ the box. Read the words across each row and ✓ the box. Then set a timer for one minute. See if you can beat the timer reading all the words in one minute. Draw a happy face when you beat the timer.

bug	lot	bark	tank	old	☐
shrug	got	lark	drank	mold	☐
slug	shot	shark	sank	told	☐
tug	rot	Mark	Hank	hold	☐
dug	cot	dark	bank	cold	☐
☐	☐	☐	☐	☐	◯

Sentence Reading: Read each sentence 3 times and cross out a sweet treat each time you read the sentence.

She wanted a sweet treat.

The sweet treat was for Moose.

She wanted a sweet treat for Moose.

She worked.

She worked with the men.

She worked with the men in the sun.

Handwriting: For each letter, letter pattern, or word, trace and then copy in the blank space. At the end of each row, draw a happy face to show that you did your best work.

look _____ book _____ ◯

her _____ u _____ g _____ ◯

F _____ all _____ B _____ e _____ ◯

Name _____

★1. FOCUS SOUND Use the Sound Card to introduce the focus sound, /o͝o/ as in book.

2. SOUND REVIEW Have students review the sounds for accuracy. **Cross Out Game:** Have students say and cross out each /o͝o/. Repeat for /er/ and /ŭŭŭ/.

er	u	g	er	f	oo		6
u	f	er	oo	u	g		12
oo	er	oo	f	g	u		18

3. SHIFTY WORD BLENDING For each word, have students say the underlined part, sound out smoothly, then read the word.

f <u>ea</u> r	<u>n</u> ea r	<u>d</u> ea r	d ea <u>l</u>

4. ACCURACY/FLUENCY For each column, have students say any underlined part, then read each word. Next, have students read the whole column.

A1 Minor-Sound Practice	B1 Sound Practice	C1 Word Endings	D1 Shifty Words	E1 Tricky Words
look	dug	<u>read</u>ing	<u>steal</u>	★ words
book	rust	<u>dreams</u>	<u>steam</u>	★ women
took	shrug	<u>treated</u>	st<u>ream</u>	★ or
	her	ta<u>ll</u>er		★ Luther
shook	after		lot	★ great
brook	under	**C2** Mixed Practice	lo<u>g</u>	
crook	leader	well	<u>frog</u>	★ were
		black		where
stood	bring	King	hot	★ where's
good	things		<u>shot</u>	
wood	wings		sh<u>eet</u>	★ other
			<u>meet</u>	★ mother
				★ brother
				★ brothers

5. PHRASES AND SENTENCES Have students read each row for accuracy, then fluency.

A	the tall men	sing songs	hit balls	in the sun

B	The tall men sing songs.

C	The tall men hit balls in the sun.

D	The tall men sing songs and hit balls in the sun.

6. MULTISYLLABIC WORDS Have students read each word part, then read each whole word.

re•mem•ber remember	un•der•stand understand	Mar•tin Martin

Unit D Activity 4
Use after Decoding Practice 3 and Chapter 1

Name _____

I listened to my partner read today's chapter. Signed _____

Story Comprehension
Young Martin Luther King Jr.

Read each sentence. Fill in the bubble for the correct answer or write the answer in the blank.
If you need to, look in your book.

1 This story is about _____

2 What could Martin do when he was little?

- ○ Martin could hit the ball far.
- ○ Martin could read.
- ○ Martin could swim in the sea.

3 Why couldn't Martin eat and drink where he wanted?

- ○ because he sang
- ○ because the car went fast
- ○ because he was black

4 What was Martin's dream?

- ○ for all men and women to be free and to be treated well
- ○ to see cats and raccoons
- ○ to go to the moon

★ **5** What did Martin Luther King dream? *(Start with Martin Luther King dreamed . . .)*

_____

_____

_____

Read and check your work. Then draw a happy face in the circle. ◯

Unit D Activity 5
Use after Decoding Practice 3 and Chapter 1

Name _____

Building Fluency

Passage Reading:
1. Read the story 2 times. Cross out a happy face each time you read the story.

Martin Luther King's Dream

Little Martin Luther King could read well.   7
"Why can't I eat there?" he said.   14
"Why can't I drink there?"   19
He could not do what he wanted.   26

Martin did not understand why.   31
He could not see why.   36
Martin's mother said, "We are black.   42
We cannot eat or drink where we want."   50

Martin wanted to eat where he wanted.   57
He wanted to drink where he wanted.   64
He wanted to do what he wanted.   71
He wanted to be free.   76

Martin Luther King had big dreams.   82
He wanted to eat where he wanted.   89
He wanted to drink where he wanted.   96
He wanted all men and women to be treated well.   106

2. Set a timer and read as far as you can in one minute.
   Cross out the timer.

Handwriting: Trace and then copy the sentence. At the end of each row, draw a happy face to show that you did your best work.

Her sister is in the sun.   ◯

◯

1. SOUND REVIEW Have students review sounds for accuracy, then for fluency.

o	u	er	i	b	l	er	7
b	ea	l	u	er	b	u	14

2. SHIFTY WORD BLENDING For each word, have students say the underlined part, sound out smoothly, then read the word.

b <u>u</u> g   <u>r</u> u g   <u>d</u> u g   d <u>i</u> g

3. ACCURACY/FLUENCY For each column, have students say any underlined part, then read each word. Next, have students read the whole column.

A1 Mixed Practice	B1 Mixed Practice	C1 Rhyming Words	D1 Shifty Words	E1 Tricky Words
dust	start	hum<u>ble</u>	<u>s</u>ing	★ others
after	ring	rum<u>ble</u>	<u>s</u>ang	★ listened
shook	free	grum<u>ble</u>	s<u>o</u>ng	★ going
until	black	stum<u>ble</u>	song<u>s</u>	
crust	shot			words
book	dreamed		well	women
buses	treated		<u>s</u>well	story
freedom	why		s<u>m</u>ell	of
				for

4. PHRASES AND SENTENCES Have students read each row for accuracy, then fluency.

A	wanted to go	work hard	it's because	little one	what's that

B	in his dream	he ran fast	with the other men

C In his dream . . .

D In his dream, he ran fast.

E In his dream, he ran fast with the other men.

5. MULTISYLLABIC WORDS Have students read each word part, then read each whole word.

un•der•stand understand	re•mem•ber remember	dif•fer•ent different

6. SOUND DICTATION Have students say and write each sound.

a. _____ b. _____ c. _____ d. _____ e. _____

7. TRICKY WORD DICTATION Have students say and spell each word, then say, spell, and write it.

a. _____ b. _____ c. _____ d. _____

Unit D Activity 6
Use after Decoding Practice 4 and Chapter 2

Name _____

I listened to my partner read today's chapter.   Signed _____

Sentences I Can Read

Fill in the bubble for the sentence that best tells about each picture.

○ She works hard in the sun.

○ Her sister looks for the star.

○ The dog runs near the moose.

○ The dog barks at Mister Brook.

○ The balls were from my friend.

○ My friend has a cat.

Story Comprehension

Read each sentence. Fill in the bubble for the answer and/or write the answer in the blank. End each sentence with a period.

1   What did Harriet Tubman do?

Harriet Tubman _____

   ○ led others to the bus

   ○ led others to freedom

   ○ led others to a sandlot

2   Tell what Harriet Tubman did.   (Start with *Harriet Tubman . . .*)

_____

_____

Unit D Activity 7
Use after Decoding Practice 4 and Chapter 2

Name _____

Story Retell
Freedom Fighter

Read the sentences and fill in the bubble for the sentence that best retells the beginning, middle, and end of the story.

BEGINNING ● **Who?**	Tell who the story is about. ● The story is about Martin Luther King. ○ The story is about the moose and the raccoon. ○ The story is about King Ben.
Want?	Tell what Martin Luther King wanted. ○ He wanted all men and women to be treated well. ○ He wanted to eat a treat. ○ He wanted to run from a friend.
MIDDLE/ ACTION ■ **What?**	Tell what happened in the middle of the story. ○ Martin and others went to see a bobcat. ○ Martin and his friends sang songs. ○ Martin and Harriet got on a bus.
END ▲ **At the End?**	Tell what happened at the end of the story. ○ Martin could see his mother in his dream. ○ Martin was shot, but we remember his dream. ○ Martin Luther King said, "I can't do this."

Handwriting Fluency

Trace the sentence.

Her sister reads thick books.

Unit E Introduction

er
as in sister

oo
as in book

u
as in umbrella

★p
as in pig

★y
as in yarn

★a
as in ago

ago along er er er y y

good hood hook took look

why what when where

Name _____

★ 1. FOCUS/REVIEW SOUNDS Use the Sound Ladder on page 49 to introduce the focus sounds, /ə/ as in ago, /y-/ as in yarn, and /p/ as in pig, and to review sounds.

2. SHIFTY WORD BLENDING For each word, have students say the underlined part, sound out smoothly, then read the word.

P i̱ p	p o̱ p	p o p s̱	p u̱ p s

3. ACCURACY/FLUENCY For each column, have students say any underlined part, then read each word. Next, have students read the whole column.

A1 Focus Sound Practice	B1 Sound Practice	C1 Rhyming Words	D1 Shifty Words	E1 Tricky Words
y̱ard	sister	coo	la̱p	★ you
y̱es	farther	goo	la̱d	★ y̱our
y̱ear			gla̱d	★ y̱ours
y̱et	muck	boom		★ y̱ourself
y̱uck	Tuck	room	ḇundle	
	Tuck's		ṯrundle	★ party
P̱ip	Tucker	bash		★ baby
p̱et	**B2** Word Endings	trash	ti̱ck	★ father
p̱est	start**ed**		tick**le**	★ birthday
shop̱	hug**s**	other	tick**les**	★ away
pi̱g	plant**s**	mother		
	book**s**	brother		great
	mean**s**			about

4. TRICKY WORD GRID (optional) Have students read the first row for accuracy, then read the entire grid for fluency.

from	for	other	were	work	5
were	other	from	work	for	10
for	were	other	from	work	15

5. PHRASES AND SENTENCES Have students read each row for accuracy, then fluency.

A	my little brother sits with me I will read a book to him
B	My little brother sits with me.
C	I will read a book to him.
D	My little brother sits with me, so I will read a book to him.

6. MULTISYLLABIC WORDS Have students read each word part, then read each whole word.

mar•ket market	gar•den•er gardener	to•geth•er together

Unit E Activity 1
Use after Decoding Practice 1 and Chapter 1

Name _____

Vocabulary

Adopt means to bring a person or pet into your family.
That person or pet becomes part of your family.

Read each sentence. Read the words above the pictures and write the word that best completes each sentence. End each sentence with a period. Circle the correct picture.

1 We will **adopt** a pet _____

2 Mom and Dad will **adopt** a little _____

stick	ball	kitten	baby
	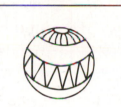		

Tricky Words

For each word, read, spell, write, and ✓. Then draw a happy face in the circle.

	Read, Spell, and ✓	Spell, Write, and ✓	Spell, Write, and ✓	Smile!
1	from ☐	_ _ _ _ ☐	_____ ☐	◯
2	other ☐	_ _ _ _ _ ☐	_____ ☐	◯
3	were ☐	_ _ _ _ ☐	_____ ☐	◯
4	work ☐	_ _ _ _ ☐	_____ ☐	◯
5	your ☐	_ _ _ _ ☐	_____ ☐	◯

 Go back to page 49

Name _____

★1. FOCUS/REVIEW SOUNDS Use the Sound Cards to introduce the focus sound, /āāā/ as in hay, and to review selected sounds.

2. SHIFTY WORD BLENDING For each word, have students say the underlined part, sound out smoothly, then read the word.

<u>a</u> sh	<u>c</u> a sh	c a s <u>t</u>	<u>bl</u> a s t

3. ACCURACY/FLUENCY For each column, have students say any underlined part, then read each word. Next, have students read the whole column.

A1 Focus Sound Practice	**B1** Sound Practice	**C1** Rhyming Words	**D1** Shifty Words	**E1** Tricky Words
<u>day</u>	year	little	<u>tee</u>	★ animals
<u>play</u>	yet	whittle	<u>hee</u>	★ people
<u>lay</u>	**B2** Rhyming Words	song	hee<u>d</u>	who
<u>a</u>cross	food	strong	nee<u>d</u>	★ who's
<u>a</u>long	mood	long	**D2** Mixed Practice	you
<u>a</u>go	go	truck	m<u>u</u>d	your
<u>a</u>dopt	so	Tuck	m<u>ar</u>ket	yourself
<u>a</u>way	no	**C2** Compound Words	sist<u>er</u>	story
	old	grandmother	s<u>ing</u>s	they
	fold	grandfather	r<u>ea</u>ds	
	gold	payday	sist<u>er</u>	
		backyard	c<u>ar</u>	
		today	f<u>un</u>	

4. PHRASES AND SENTENCES Have students read each row for accuracy, then fluency.

Ⓐ	let's adopt animals	for Grandfather	and Grandmother
Ⓑ	Let's adopt animals.		
Ⓒ	Let's adopt animals for Grandfather.		
Ⓓ	Let's adopt animals for Grandfather and Grandmother.		

5. MULTISYLLABIC WORDS Have students read each word part, then read each whole word.

gar•den	garden	pep•per•mint	peppermint
dif•fer•ent	different	yes•ter•day	yesterday
Ber•tha	Bertha	in•ter•est•ing	interesting

Name _____

I listened to my partner read today's chapter.   Signed _____

Rhyming Patterns

For each box, read the rhyming pattern and circle the two sounds that go with the pattern to make real words. Write the real words. Read the words to yourself.

(d) x̶ (pl)	s th b	r w sm
ay	**ink**	**ell**
d̶ _____	_____	_____
p̶l̶ _____	_____	_____

Sentence Jumble

Use the words in each box to make a sentence. Start each sentence with a capital letter. End each sentence with a period.

wanted a sweet treat Grandfather	_____ _____ _____

went Grandfather and I to the market	_____ _____ _____

Read the sentences. Draw a happy face if they make sense.

Unit E Activity 3
Use after Decoding Practice 2 and Chapter 3

Name _____

Building Fluency

Sentence Reading: Read each sentence 3 times and cross out a party hat each time you read the sentence.

See my little brother.

See my little brother Tuck go!

Pip can read a book.

Pip can read a book to Tuck.

We need snacks.

We need snacks for Tuck.

We need snacks for Tuck's birthday party.

Do you need snacks?

Do you need snacks for the party?

Do you need snacks for the party for Tuck?

Handwriting: For each letter, letter pattern, or word, trace and then copy in the blank space. At the end of each row, draw a happy face to show that you did your best work.

ay ___ ay ___ p ___ p ___

ago ___ look ___ y ___

er ___ ar ___ u ___ f ___

Unit E Decoding Practice 3
Use with Little Brother Tuck, Chapter 3

Name _____

1. SOUND REVIEW Have students review the sounds for accuracy. **Cross Out Game:** Have students say and cross out each /āāā/ as in hay. Repeat for /p/ as in pig and /ə/ as in ago.

u	p	ay	y	a	y	6
p	u	g	ay	p	ay	12
ay	p	u	g	ay	y	18

2. SHIFTY WORD BLENDING For each word, have students say the underlined part, sound out smoothly, then read the word.

t o ss	l o ss	l o s t

3. ACCURACY/FLUENCY For each column, have students say any underlined part, then read each word. Next, have students read the whole column.

A1 Sound Practice	B1 Mixed Practice	C1 Sound Practice	D1 Rhyming Words	E1 Tricky Words
add	why	too	day	★ find
crab	clam	boo	clay	★ word
bash	spoon	food		birthday
Dad's	grin		look	animals
	drink	**C2** Mixed Practice	book	people
across	today	dip	**D2** Word Endings	they
asleep	last	peek	plays	who's
along		list	played	you
away		buns	picks	your
		kids	gets	yourself
		hip		for

4. PHRASES AND SENTENCES Have students read each row for accuracy, then fluency.

A	I was	at a loss	my best friend	went away

B I was at a loss.

C My best friend went away.

D I was at a loss when my best friend went away.

5. MULTISYLLABIC WORDS Have students read each word part, then read each whole word.

nap•kins napkins	shop•ping shopping	in•sect insect
hoo•ray hooray		tea•spoon•ful teaspoonful

Unit E Activity 4
Use after Decoding Practice 3 and Chapter 3

Name _____

I listened to my partner read today's chapter. Signed _____

Story Comprehension
At the Market

Read each sentence. Fill in the bubble for the answer or write the answer in the blank. If you need to, look in your book.

1 This story is about _____ , _____ ,

and _____ .

2 Who was in the shopping cart?

　　O Mom was in the shopping cart with Pip.
　　O Pip and Tuck were in the shopping cart.
　　O Tuck was in the shopping cart.

3 What was on the long list?

　　O hot cats and rats
　　O books and books
　　O hot dogs and buns

1. hot dogs and buns
2. crab and clams
3. drinks
4. cups, spoons, napkins
5. hats

4 What did Mom get for Tuck?

　　O a hot dog in a bun
　　O a cup for the drinks
　　O a fun book

5 Tell what Mom got for Tuck. (Start with *Mom got . . .*) _____

_____

_____

Read and check your work. Then draw a happy face in the circle.

Unit E Activity 5
Use after Decoding Practice 3 and Chapter 3

Name _____

Building Fluency

Passage Reading:

1. Read the story 2 times. Cross out a cake each time you read the story.

To Market, To Market

    Little Tuck, Mom, and Pip go to the market. Mom   10
needs food for the birthday party. Mom has a long   20
list. Boo hoo. Mom cannot find hot dogs and dip.   30

    To market, to market, little Tucker, Mom, and Pip.   39
To market, to market, to get hot dogs and dip.   49

    To market, to market, little Tucker, Mom, and Pip.   58
To market, to market, hooray, hip, hip.   65

    To market, to market, little Tucker, Mom, and Pip.   74
To market, to market, no hot dogs and dip?   83

    To market, to market, Little Tucker, Mom, and Pip.   92
To market, to market, sad, sad, little Pip.   100

---

2. Set a timer and read as far as you can in one minute.
   Cross out the timer.

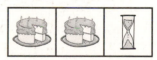

Handwriting: Trace and then copy the sentence. At the end of each row, draw a happy face to show that you did your best work.

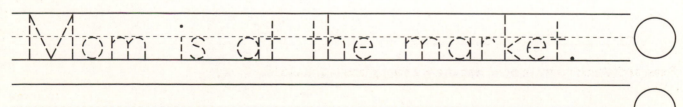

Name _____

1. SOUND REVIEW Have students review sounds for accuracy, then for fluency.

b	p	y	g	ay	p	ay	7
g	y	p	y	g	ay	b	14

2. SHIFTY WORD BLENDING For each word, have students say the underlined part, sound out smoothly, then read the word.

s <u>ay</u>	<u>d</u> ay	<u>w</u> ay	<u>p l</u> ay

3. ACCURACY/FLUENCY For each column, have students say any underlined part, then read each word. Next, have students read the whole column.

A1 Mixed Practice	B1 Mixed Practice	C1 Multisyllabic Words	D1 Shifty Words	E1 Tricky Words
today	starts	Tucker	ba<u>sh</u>	said
ago	pick	adopted	ba<u>t</u>	you
year	brings	birthday	b<u>e</u>t	one
Peg	send	recall	be<u>st</u>	his
yum	gift	upset	**D2** Word Endings	are
peek	keep	sister	be	friend
glad	best	crying	being	your
				birthday

4. PHRASES AND SENTENCES Have students read each row for accuracy, then fluency.

A	there it is	we are glad	bring it	pick it up	my best friend
B	Pip and Tuck		got that gift		one year ago
C	Pip and Tuck . . .
D	Pip and Tuck got that gift.
E	Pip and Tuck got that gift one year ago.

5. MULTISYLLABIC WORDS Have students read each word part, then read each whole word.

re•call•ing	recalling	a•dopt•ing	adopting

6. SOUND DICTATION Have students say and write each sound.

a. _____ b. _____ c. _____ d. _____ e. _____

7. TRICKY WORD DICTATION Have students say and spell each word, then say, spell, and write it.

a. _____ b. _____ c. _____ d. _____

Unit E Activity 6
Use after Decoding Practice 4 and Chapter 4

Name _____

I listened to my partner read today's chapter.   Signed _____

Phrases I Can Read

Fill in the bubble for the words that best tell about each picture.

	○ pigs singing ○ pigs sitting
	○ cars skidding ○ parked cars
	○ trucks in muck ○ tricks in muck
	○ boots in the truck ○ boots in the muck

Tricky Words in Sentences

Read each sentence. Fill in the bubble for the correct answer and write the word in the blank.

1   Is this _____ treat?
    ○ you   ○ your   ○ they

2   What day of the week is _____?
    ○ today   ○ they   ○ his

3   _____ in the mud?
    ○ Who's   ○ Who   ○ Story

Name _____

Story Retell
Little Brother Tuck

Fill in the bubble for the sentence that best retells the beginning, middle, and end of the story. Then read and illustrate each part of the story.

BEGINNING ● **Who?**	Tell who the story is about. ○ The story is about Pip and Tuck. ○ The story is about a truck and a pig. ○ The story is about Pip's big brother.
MIDDLE/ ACTION ■ **What Happened?**	Tell what happened in the middle of the story. ○ Pip went to see Grandmother Bertha. ○ Mom, Pip, and Tuck went to the sandlot to see Rod. ○ Mom, Pip, and Tuck went to the market. ○ The party started, and Tucker was crying. ○ The party started, and Pip was crying. ○ The party started, and Tucker got gifts.
END ▲ **At the End?**	Tell what happened at the end of the story. ○ Mom and Dad said, "Pip, you are the best sister. This is your party too." ○ Mom and Dad said, "Pip, you are not the best sister. There is no gift for you."

Handwriting Fluency

Trace the sentence.